CW00536529

How Things Move

Making Things Move

Siân Smith

www.heinemannlibrary.co.uk
Visit our website to find out more information about Heinemann Library books.

To order:
☎ Phone 44 (0) 1865 888066
Send a fax to 44 (0) 1865 314091
Visit the Heinemann Bookshop at www.heinemannlibrary.co.uk to browse our catalogue and order online.

Heinemann Library is an imprint of Capstone Global Library Limited, a company incorporated in England and Wales having its registered office at 7 Pilgrim Street, London, EC4V 6LB – Registered company number: 6695582

Heinemann is a registered trademark of Pearson Education Limited, under licence to Capstone Global Library Limited

Edited by Sian Smith, Rebecca Rissman, and Charlotte Guillain
Designed by Joanna Hinton-Malivoire
Picture research by Elizabeth Alexander and Maria Joannou
Production by Duncan Gilbert
Originated by Dot Gradations Ltd
Printed and bound in China by South China Printing Company Ltd

ISBN 978 0 431 19389 2 (hardback)
13 12 11 10 09
10 9 8 7 6 5 4 3 2 1

British Library Cataloguing in Publication Data
Smith, Sîan
Making things move. - (Acorn plus. How things move)
1. Force and energy - Juvenile literature
I. Title
531.6

Acknowledgements
We would like to thank the following for permission to reproduce photographs: ©Alamy p.**18** (Ilene MacDonald); ©Capstone Global Library Ltd. pp.**12**, **13**, **14**, **15**, **20**, **21** (Tudor Photography 2008); ©Corbis pp.**19** (Ben Blankenburg), **10 bottom right** (image100), **7** (Judith Haeusler/Zefa), **11** (Susanne Dittrich/Zefa); ©Getty Images p.**6** (DK Stock/Guillermo Hung); ©Photolibrary pp.**22** (Flirt Collection/Jose Inc), **16** (OSF/Rob Nunnington), **17** (Robert Harding Travel/Mark Chivers); © Rex Features p.**10 top left** (Image Source), **10 bottom left** (WestEnd61); © Shutterstock pp.**4 left** (Abramova Kseniya), **5 bottom right** (Charles Taylor), **5 bottom right** (Chen Wei Seng), **4 right** (Juris Sturainis), **5 top right** (Laurie Search), **5 top left** (Orientaly), **9** (Stefanie Angele), **8** (Thomas Mounsey)

Cover photograph of a bowling pin strike reproduced with permission of ©Corbis (Mark Cooper). Back cover photograph of leaves reproduced with permission of ©Shutterstock (Stefanie Angele).

Every effort has been made to contact copyright holders of material reproduced in this book. Any omissions will be rectified in subsequent printings if notice is given to the publishers.

Contents

Some words are shown in bold, **like this.** They are explained in "Words to know" on page 23.

Moving fast and slow

Things can move at different **speeds.**

Things can move fast.

Things can move slowly.

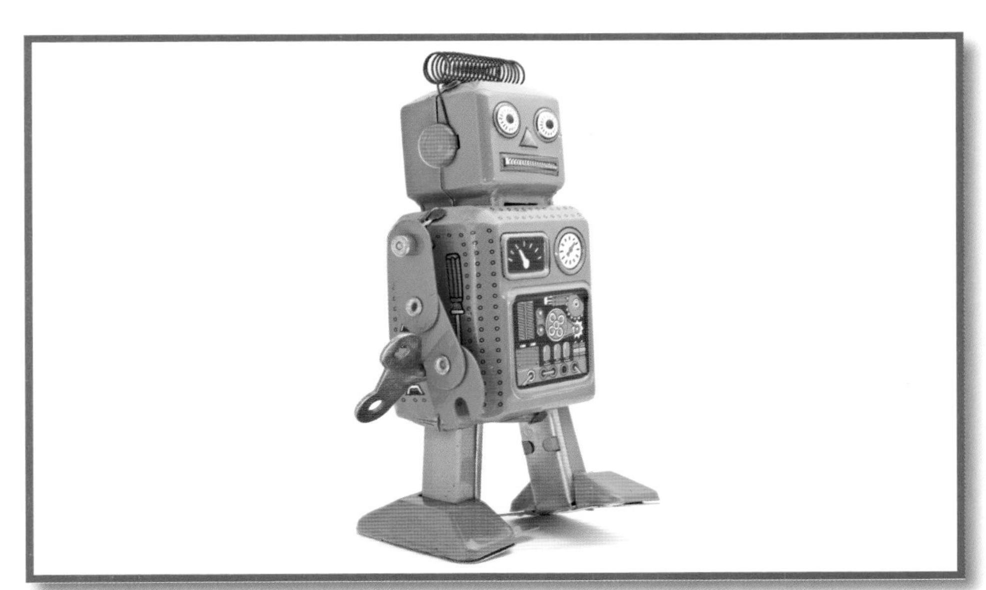

Which things are moving fast in these pictures?

Which things are moving slowly?

How do things move?

Things start moving when they are given a **push** or a **pull**. We can make things move with pushes and pulls.

A pull can make something move towards you.
A push can make something move away from you.

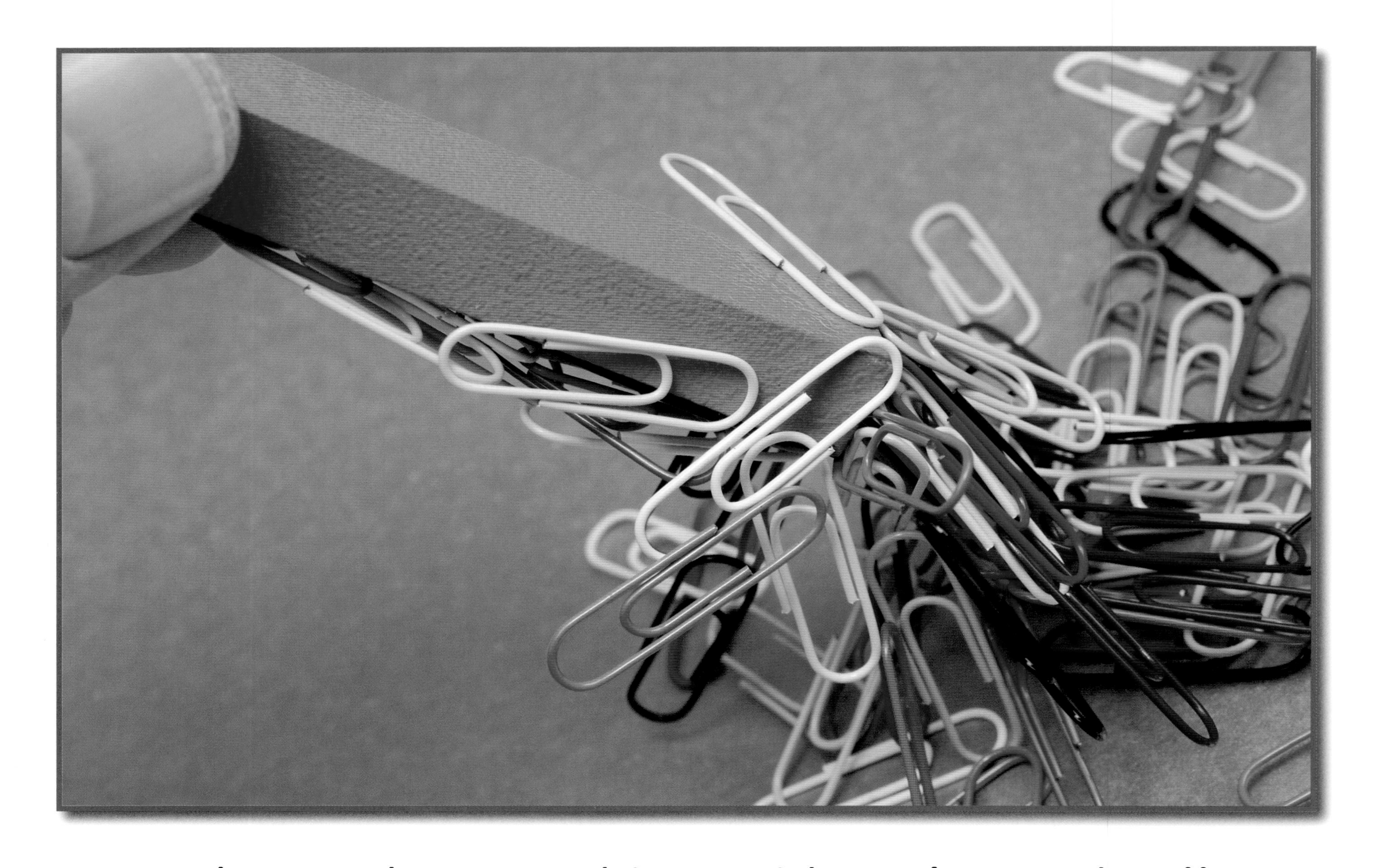

Not only people move things with **pushes and pulls.**

A magnet can pull things.

A magnet can make a paper clip move with a pull.

The wind can push things. The wind can make leaves move with a push.

Which pictures show things being **pushed**? Which pictures show things being **pulled**?

Pushes and pulls are both **forces**.

A force can be a push or a pull that works to make something move.

How fast? How far?

This boy is giving the ball a small **push**.

How fast do you think the ball will go?

How far do you think the ball will move?

A small push made the ball move slowly.

A small push did not move the ball very far.

The same boy is giving the ball a big **push**.

How fast do you think the ball will go?

How far do you think the ball will move?

A big push made the ball move faster.

A big push made the ball move **further**.

A big **pull** can make something move faster than a small pull. A big pull can make something move **further** than a small pull.

Will this pull make the boat go fast?

Will this pull make the boat go far?

Stopping

We can start things moving with a **push** or a **pull**.

We can stop things moving with a push or a pull, too.

This girl started the ball moving with a push.
The goalkeeper will stop the ball moving with a push.

Changing direction

The way something is going is called its **direction**. It might be going up, or down, forwards, or backwards, left, or right. This yo-yo is going down.

Pushes and **pulls** can make things change direction. When we pull a yo-yo it stops going down and starts to move up instead.

Push or pull?

This boy changed the **direction** of the ball.

Did he change it with a **push** or a **pull**?

Words to know

direction	the way something is going. For example, something might be moving backwards, forwards, up, down, left, or right.
distance	how far something has moved
force	something that can make things start moving, stop moving, speed up, slow down, or change direction. Pushes and pulls are forces.
further	greater distance
pull	force that can make something move towards you
push	force that can make something move away from you
speed	how quickly or slowly something is moving

Index

Notes for parents and teachers

Before reading

Using a soft ball demonstrate how you can move it with different actions. Encourage the children to use the words "pushing" and "pulling". Talk about moving the ball in different directions – up, down, forwards, backwards, sideways, and diagonally. Roll the ball and stop it with your hand. Talk about stopping a movement. Invite a child to move the ball in some way. The other children should name the action.

After reading

- Create a simple chart. Draw five objects down the left hand side of the board. (For example, a ball, a brick, a car, a teddy, a beaker.) At the top of the chart write: Easy to push/Easy to pull/ Goes fast/Goes slowly. Ask the children to consider each object and to decide where to put a tick or a cross.
- Help the children to make a class book about how things move. Talk about the contents (pulling, pushing, changing direction, fast and slow). Let each child choose a movement and draw a picture to illustrate it. (For example, a fast aeroplane.) Then support each child to write a caption, for example: "This aeroplane goes fast.", "You can pull this kite string.".